KAWASE HASUI
COLORING BOOK

Kawase Hasui was born in Tokyo in 1883. His parents were merchants, but after trying his hand at the family business, Hasui decided it wasn't for him. Instead, at the age of twenty-five he began studying art at the school of master Japanese painter Kaburagi Kiyokata, where his great talent soon became apparent. In 1916 he met publisher Watanabe Shozaburo, who began turning Hasui's watercolor paintings into woodblock prints for sale on the world market. The prints became especially popular in the United States and made Hasui famous and financially successful. His pictures showed scenes of rural Japan, often emphasizing the seasons: flowers in spring, bright sunshine in summer, turning leaves in fall, and snow scenes in winter. In 1956, near the end of his life, the Japanese government honored Hasui as a "Living National Treasure."

This coloring book holds twenty-two of Hasui's beautiful images that have been traced for you to color. The full-color originals are shown as small pictures on the inside front and back covers. When you color in the tracings, you can copy Hasui's original colors and style, or you might decide to try something completely different. The last page of the book is blank so you can draw and color your own picture—perhaps a view of your backyard or a nearby park. Can you capture the feeling of the season the way Hasui did?

Pomegranate **Kids** ®
AGES 3 to 103!

The original artworks are by Kawase Hasui (Japanese, 1883–1957), courtesy Castle Fine Arts, Inc.

1. *Agatsuma Gorge,* 1947. Woodblock print, 15½ x 10½ in. (39.4 x 26.7 cm).

2. *Evening at Kintai Bridge*, 1947. Woodblock print, 15½ x 10½ in. (39.4 x 26.7 cm).

3. *Lake Matsubara, Morning, Shinshu*, 1941. Woodblock print, 10½ x 15½ in. (26.7 x 39.4 cm).

4. *Spring Night at Inokashira*, 1931. Woodblock print, 15½ x 10½ in. (39.4 x 26.7 cm).

5. *Autumn at Funatsu near Lake Kawaguchi*, c. 1945. Woodblock print, 10½ x 15½ in. (26.7 x 39.4 cm).

6. *Ferry at Yoshino River in Spring*, 1950. Woodblock print, 10½ x 15½ in. (26.7 x 39.4 cm).

7. *Ginkakuji Temple, Kyoto, in Snow*, 1951. Woodblock print, 15½ x 10½ in. (39.4 x 26.7 cm).

8. *Kasuga Shrine, Nara, in Rain*, 1933. Woodblock print, 15½ x 10½ in. (39.4 x 26.7 cm).

9. *Senju Waterfall, Akame*, 1951. Woodblock print, 15½ x 10½ in. (39.4 x 26.7 cm).

10. *Tengu Rock, Shiobara*, 1952. Woodblock print, 15½ x 10½ in. (39.4 x 26.7 cm).

11. *Autumn at Saruiwa, Shiobara*, 1949. Woodblock print, 15½ x 10½ in. (39.4 x 26.7 cm).

12. *Daigo Denpo Temple, Kyoto*, 1950. Woodblock print, 15½ x 10½ in. (39.4 x 26.7 cm).

13. *Ueno Toshogu Shrine in Spring*, 1948. Woodblock print, 15½ x 10½ in. (39.4 x 26.7 cm).

14. *Kumamoto Castle in Samidare*, 1948. Woodblock print, 15½ x 10½ in. (39.4 x 26.7 cm)

15. *The Yama Temple, Sendai*, 1933. Woodblock print, 15½ x 10½ in. (39.4 x 26.7 cm).

16. *Mt. Fuji Seen from Oshino*, 1942. Woodblock print, 15½ x 10½ in. (39.4 x 26.7 cm).

17. *Full Moon at Izu-ura, Ibaraki*, 1952. Woodblock print, 10½ x 15½ in. (26.7 x 39.4 cm).

18. *Iris Garden at Meiji Shrine, Tokyo*, 1951. Woodblock print, 15½ x 10½ in. (39.4 x 26.7 cm).

19. *Morning at Mitohama*, 1952. Woodblock print, 15½ x 10½ in. (39.4 x 26.7 cm).

20. *Nikko Shin-kyo (Shin Bridge, Nikko)*, 1951. Woodblock print, 10½ x 15½ in. (26.7 x 39.4 cm).

21. *Mt. Fuji Seen from the River Banyu*, 1931. Woodblock print, 10½ x 15½ in. (26.7 x 39.4 cm).

22. *The Great Buddha, Kamakura*, 1930. Woodblock print, 15½ x 10 in. (39.4 x 25.4 cm).

Pomegranate Communications, Inc.
19018 NE Portal Way, Portland OR 97230
800 227 1428   www.pomegranate.com

Color illustrations © 2014 Kawase Fumiko and S. Watanabe Color Print Co.,
courtesy of Castle Fine Arts, Inc. ▪ www.castlefinearts.com
Line drawings © Pomegranate Communications, Inc.

Item No. CB159

Designed by Carey Hall. Line drawings by LeeAnne Gibney.

Printed in Korea

23 22 21 20 19 18 17 16 15 14   10 9 8 7 6 5 4 3 2 1

Distributed by Pomegranate Europe Ltd.
Unit 1, Heathcote Business Centre, Hurlbutt Road
Warwick, Warwickshire CV34 6TD, UK
[+44] 0 1926 430111
sales@pomeurope.co.uk

1. *Agatsuma Gorge*

2. Evening at Kintai Bridge

3. Lake Matsubara, Morning, Shinshu

4. Spring Night at Inokashira

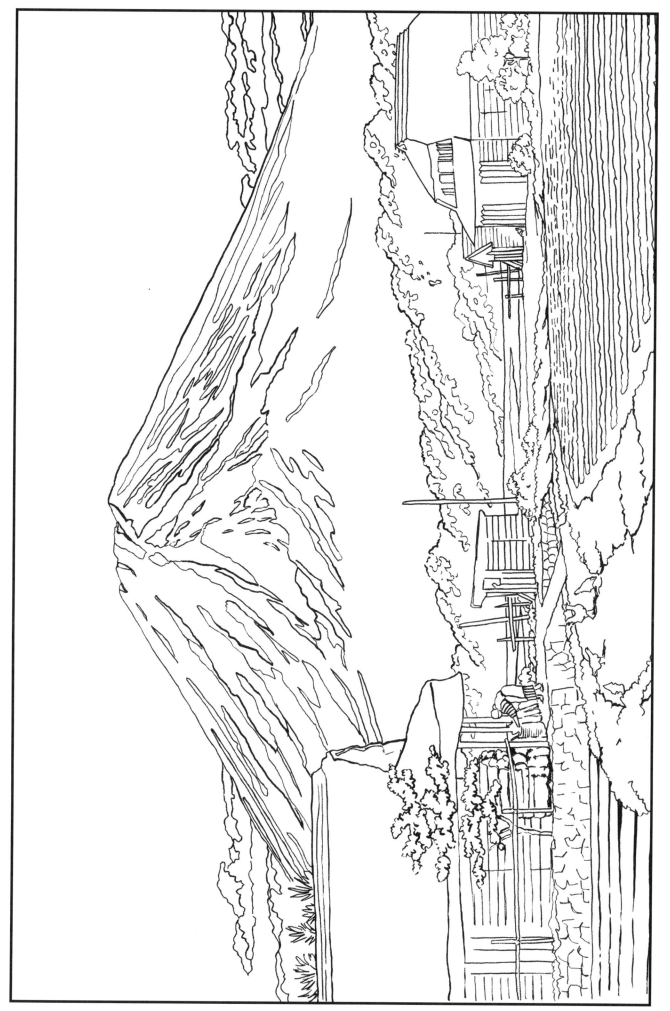

5. *Autumn at Funatsu near Lake Kawaguchi*

6. Ferry at Yoshino River in Spring

7. Ginkakuji Temple, Kyoto, in Snow

8. Kasuga Shrine, Nara, in Rain

9. Senju Waterfall, Akame

10. *Tengu Rock, Shiobara*

11. Autumn at Saruiwa, Shiobara

12. *Daigo Denpo Temple, Kyoto*

13. *Ueno Toshogu Shrine in Spring*

14. *Kumamoto Castle in Samidare*

15. *The Yama Temple, Sendai*

16. *Mt. Fuji Seen from Oshino*

17. Full Moon at Izu-ura, Ibaraki

18. Iris Garden at Meiji Shrine, Tokyo

19. Morning at Mitohama

20. *Nikko Shin-kyo (Shin Bridge, Nikko)*

21. Mt. Fuji Seen from the River Banyu

22. *The Great Buddha, Kamakura*

Draw and color your own picture here!